SOLDERING AND BRAZING

SOLDERING

AND

BRAZING

by

A. R. TURPIN

Illustrated by the Author

MODEL & ALLIED PUBLICATIONS
ARGUS BOOKS LIMITED
14 St. James Road, Watford
Herts.

Model and Allied Publications
Argus Books Limited
14 St. James Road, Watford
Herts., England

First Published 1955
Second Impression (revised) 1963
Third Impression 1967
Fourth Impression 1970
Fifth Impression 1972
Sixth Impression 1973
Seventh Impression 1975
Eighth Impression 1976
Ninth Impression 1980

ISBN 0 85344 098 0

Printed and bound in Great Britain
by
WOOD WESTWORTH
St. Helens, Merseyside

ACKNOWLEDGMENTS

MUCH of the knowledge in this book has been learnt from others; from their writing, from what they have told me, or from just watching some craftsman at work; and most of these must be nameless for no other reason than that I have forgotten their names—if I ever knew them. I do, however, thank all those firms who have so kindly supplied me with data and photographs to illustrate particular items in this book, and in such cases I have given due credit in the text.

I would especially like to thank the Tin Research Institute for permission to use certain information from their publications by W. R. Lewis, B.Sc.(Lond.), most of the information on the strength of solders coming from this source.

Also I would thank the Education Officer of the London County Council and Mr. Elms for permission to photograph the operations of wiping a joint as practised at the Brixton School of Building.

Finally, my thanks to Mr. R. D. Strauss, A.I.M., for reading the proofs.

CONTENTS

Silver Soldering a 3½″ Gauge Locomotive Boiler

INTRODUCTION

In this book there are chapters devoted to soft and hard solders, fluxes, heating devices, and the practical application ; and to the man who merely wishes to solder a patch on the bottom of the kettle, all this may be a little confusing, especially if he has never held a soldering iron in his hand before. So to him, and others like him, I would say skip those first chapters and get down to the practical side of the book and simply buy himself a six-ounce soldering iron, a few sticks of blowpipe solder and a tin of " Baker's " or similar flux, using an ordinary gas ring, or bunsen burner, to heat the iron.

If it is radio repairs that the reader wishes to carry out then get himself a three-ounce iron and a reel of 60/40 resin-cored solder, and go ahead. The chapters on solders and fluxes can be read later when that urgent job has been done, and the worker's interest has been aroused. He will most likely want to know if there is not a stronger solder for certain jobs ; or a more efficient flux for certain metals ; and if he reads those other chapters he will find that there most likely is.

A definition of soldering or brazing could be given as follows : — " The joining of two metals by means of a metallic alloy or solder, which has a lower melting point than the metals to be joined. The joint surfaces of the two metals are mechanically or chemically cleaned, the oxide film removed or prevented from forming by means of a flux, and the two metals and the solder heated until the latter melts, and is drawn into the joint by capillary attraction ; the solder then alloys with the two metals, properly ' wetting ' them, and forming an atomic bond. The solder is then allowed to cool and solidify, thus joining the metals permanently together."

To distinguish brazing from bronze welding, it should be pointed out that in the latter case the molten metal from a fused filler rod is placed in an open joint, and is not drawn into it by capillary attraction.

Lead will not easily alloy with copper but tin will do so. If a piece of copper is mechanically cleaned and fluxed, and a pool of molten lead poured on to it, and then wiped off whilst still molten, it will be found that it has only " wetted " the copper in patches ; and even in these patches the adherence of the lead to the copper is more of a mechanical, than an alloying one. But if an alloy of tin and lead in, say, equal proportions is melted and poured on a similar piece of metal, and is then wiped off the surface of the copper whilst it is still molten it will be impossible to remove it completely and a thin skin will remain, consisting of an alloy of the solder and the copper. When this skin is present the copper is said to be properly " wetted " or " tinned."

Soldering can roughly be divided into three categories : — (1) Soft soldering, using alloys having melting points ranging from 70° C. to 400° C.; (2) Hard solders, with melting points ranging from 400° C. to 800° C.; (3) Brasses used for brazing, with melting points between 800° C. and 1,083° C., the melting point of copper. The usual, accepted demarcation between hard solders and brasses is that the former are chiefly silver alloys and the latter zinc-copper alloys.

also advantageous in this case because the eutectic alloy has the lowest melting point of tin-lead solders and this is important when soldering delicate components that are likely to be damaged by heat. But a small plastic range has been found to be an advantage; it appears to prevent fractures at the time of soldering caused by vibration, especially on automatic soldering machines, and for this reason 60/40 solder is more popular than 63/37.

The viscosity of a solder is important for two reasons : firstly, one of high viscosity will not run into a very close joint; secondly, the soldering iron will carry more solder to the joint which may mean a stronger joint and therefore desirable, or that more solder is being used than is necessary and undesirable. Both points must be considered. The viscosity of a solder increases with the lead content.

The strength of a solder cannot be given in one characteristic figure but is the composite of a number of qualities which follow :—

Shear Strength. This has to be taken into consideration when a pipe is soldered into a socket, or a straight pull applied to a lap joint. (See Fig. 2.)

Tensile Strength. When a straight pull is given to two rods, or sheets, butt jointed together.

Elongation, or ductility. Which is required in a solder when the joint has to be hammered into shape or cold worked; a property not often required in soft solders.

Impact Strength. When a blow is struck sideways on a butt joint.

The above are the main factors to be considered but more than one characteristic is likely to be involved in every joint to a greater or lesser degree.

The strength of a joint does not depend entirely on the strength of a particular solder, but also on such things as good tinning, flux inclusions, joint space, etc.

When using soft solders it will be found that in nearly all

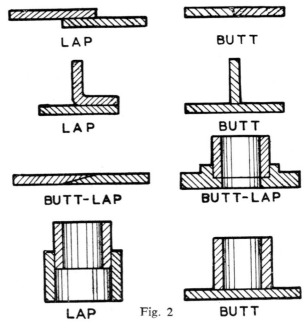

LAP   BUTT

LAP   BUTT

BUTT-LAP   BUTT-LAP

LAP   Fig. 2   BUTT

joints the most important strength characteristic is the shear strength, and in Fig. 3 the shear strength in tons per square inch is plotted against solders of different tin-lead percentages.   It will be seen that it rises to a maximum strength opposite the eutectic alloy, after which it falls. This curve is for pure tin-lead solders, and the falling off of strength is not so apparent in the less pure commercial solders, but a definite increase in strength can be made to the solder by the addition of up to 6% of antimony of the *tin* content; but what is more important about this addition is that the falling off of strength after the maximum has been reached does not occur but remains at the maximum figure.

However, it is not advisable to use antimonial solders on zinc or brass, because there is a danger of the joints becoming brittle owing to zinc-antimony compounds forming.

The cost of tin has fluctuated in recent years between five and ten times the cost of lead, and the price has risen

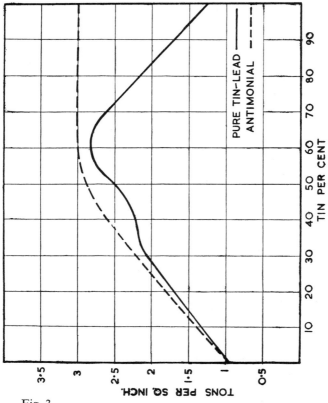

Fig. 3

as much as 500% in the last ten years. This means that recently the cost has been a far greater factor in determining the tin-lead ratio than it was ten years ago. The predominant alloy is now 40/60, whereas a few years ago 50/50 was the usual alloy, at least for blowpipe solder. But the cost of the solder is not the final cost, and it should be realised that if a quick setting solder like 60/40 is used, not only are man hours saved but as this solder is stronger than 40/60 then less solder is required on the joint and material is saved ; this latter saving being automatic because the richer tin solder will have less viscosity and less solder will be carried to the joint. So that by using a solder richer in tin, both man hours and solder will be saved and the job may work out cheaper. Finally, with a rich tin solder a good joint is more certain, and the cost of failures caused by poor joints is also reduced.

The electrical conductivity is also very important in certain types of electrical work, such as in the construction of electric motors and generators, which, in the large sizes, may contain a very great number of joints. The figures for electrical conductivity are shown in Table No. 1.

Anyone wishing to experiment with different alloys can obtain pure tin in granule form from Messrs. Johnson, Matthey & Co. Ltd. The lead used need not be pure, but should be reasonably so ; lead roofing is usually suitable but not all piping, and some used for casting laboratory apparatus and the like may contain a high percentage of antimony, and for the same reason lead from car batteries is not ideal.

The antimony content should never exceed 7% of the tin content.

At temperatures over 80° C. the strength of solder is greatly reduced, and this should be borne in mind when making joints in hot water systems and the like ; the pipe should never hang from the top joint but be supported from the bottom one. There are obtainable specially high-melting

Plate No. 1. Types of "Solon" electric soldering irons

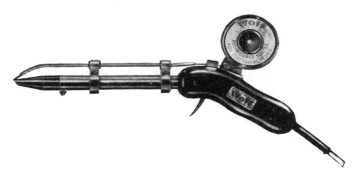

Plate No. 2. The "Wolf" Automatic soldergun type 51

Plate No. 3. The "Adcola" pencil soldering iron in use

Plate No. 4. The Mullard ultrasonic soldering iron

point solders, alloys of silver-lead-tin, and silver-cadmium having melting points ranging from 296° C. to 390° C., and tensile strengths varying from 2.5 to 8.4 tons per square inch. It should be remembered that an ordinary electric soldering iron will be of no use when using such high melting point solders. Frys Metal Foundries Ltd. market a number of high temperature soft solders, such as their H.T.3, and so do Johnson Matthey Ltd., whose "Comsol" solder is marketed by Multicore Solders Ltd., also Enthoven & Sons Ltd. manufactures them.

The important point to be noted with their high melting point solders is not their initial strength, but their strength at elevated temperatures. A comparison with 50/50 and H.T.3 is as follows: 50/50 at 20° C., 2.5 tons sq. in.; H.T.3, 3 tons sq. in.; and at 150° C., 0.75 and 1.75 tons respectively.

Solders used for wiping joints are usually of a 30-70 tin-lead alloy because this has a very long plastic range of 74° C., which gives the operator plenty of time to form a joint.

Solder used for metal spraying usually has a very low tin content, but this method of using lead solder has a very high health hazard unless the correct precautions are taken, and before using this process an expert should be consulted.

Solders used on zinc base die castings should be of cadmium-zinc-eutectic alloy 82.5/17.5, with a melting point of 264° C. No flux is used, or ordinary solder used with Fry's Metal Foundries special flux S.35.

Solder for aluminium is 95/5 tin-zinc; tin-lead solders corrode badly, or use Fry's "Fregal," or "L.M." without flux. Details are given in Chapter 5.

On occasions it is necessary to solder articles that will not stand a lot of heat, and low melting point solders must be used, but some of these can only be used on pre-tinned surfaces. Two such solders are as follows: Bismuth, 50%; lead, 25%; tin, 12.5%; cadmium, 12.5%. This is known as

Woods metal and has a melting point as low as 70° C.; this tins easily with all types of flux. This solder is useful for making joints in glass apparatus that need to be vacuum tight and also for joining metal and glass and other vitreous materials. A low melting point solder for pewter consists of Bismuth, 50%; tin, 25%; lead, 25%, with a melting point of 113° C.

Fry's Metal Foundries, Ltd., and Enthoven & Son Ltd., manufacture a number of such solders.

When soldering food containers great care must be taken so that the solder does not contaminate the food, and 60/40 solders should be used on seams if only a very fine edge of solder is in contact with the food; otherwise a pure tin solder should be specified.

For actual tinning of the inside of kitchen or dairy utensils only pure tin should be used, at least 99% pure; anything less refined is definitely dangerous.

Pure tin solder paint is excellent for tinning " one off " jobs.

Solders with very low tin contents have been found to have a better fatigue strength at elevated temperatures than some richer alloys and are being used to a large extent to solder car radiators.

The more popular solders can be obtained in a number of physical shapes, some of which are set out below.

Tinman's sticks	¼lb. and ½lb.	16" x ¼"
Blowpipe	2 oz. sticks.	24" x ¼"
Wire	Various size bobbins	6 S.W.G. to 22 S.W.G.
Cored wire	Various size bobbins	6 S.W.G. to 22 S.W.G.
Tape	Reels	1" x 0.01" to 0.005"
Core tape	Reels	1" and ½"
Nuggets	1lb. and 2lb.	
Ingots	7, 12 and 14lb.	
Plumber's sticks	1lb.	12" x 1¼" x ¼"

Cored solders are wire or tape solders with core of flux, the percentage by weight of the core being from 2 to 3.5%.

Paint or paste solders consist of solders in a fine powder form mixed with a liquid flux to form a thick paste or paint.

Solder powders are finely ground solder mixed with a powder flux.

Stick solder-flux is as above but with the powders compressed into a stick.

The paint solder mentioned above is solder in a form that is becoming more and more popular, and is manufactured by a number of firms in a number of alloys, and one which is pure tin; this can be used for tinning food containers. The model engineer will also find paint solder useful when reproducing galvanized objects on a small scale; it can also be used to protect the cut edges of tin plate by re-tinning them. Most of the fluxes used with paint solders are corrosive and should be removed by washing. Some of them are excellent for tinning cast iron. Paints with non-corrosive flux are also obtainable, such as Fry's Alcho-Re-solder Cream.

A comparatively new production is the coloured cored solder introduced by H. J. Enthoven & Sons Ltd. This solder has a flux core that leaves a coloured flux residue on the joint and this can have a number of useful purposes. It can be used to identify the alloy of the solder, or as an indication that the joint has been soldered. It can be used to identify the department soldering the joint, or as an indication of polarity, voltage or frequency of that portion of the circuit, etc., etc. These solders are at present available in four colours to order.

The price of solder not only varies with the tin content but also according to the physical form in which it has been manufactured, i.e., wire, stick, paste, etc.

The owner of a small workshop, having read the foregoing, may feel rather bewildered as to the type of solder with which to equip himself, and the following suggestions are therefore made.

For general use a few sticks of blowpipe solder 40/60 tin-lead, and for electrical work, such as servicing radio sets and electric motor repairs, 60/40 non-corrosive cored solder. Solder paint will also be found to be extremely useful, in fact, the most useful in the small workshop.

The names and addresses of a number of solder manufacturers are given at the end of the book.

CHAPTER 2

HARD SOLDERS AND BRAZING STRIP

ALTHOUGH there is no real demarcation line between hard solders and brasses, an approximate division can be made as follows; hard solders 400° C. to 750° C. and brazing strip 750° C. to 1,083° C., the melting point of copper. It will be appreciated that with these higher melting points, soldering irons cannot be used but a torch, or oven, will be necessary.

The difference between hard solders and brazing strip is that the former usually contain silver and the latter are usually simple alloys of copper and zinc. The process of joining metals with silver solders is usually referred to as hard soldering and when using brazing strip as brazing, although there is no hard and fast demarcation and the procedure is the same in both cases.

The points to be considered when choosing hard solders are rather different from those that were discussed with reference to soft solders, and are as follows: (1) Melting Point. (2) Plastic Range. (3) Strength. (4) Cost. (5) Self Fluxing Properties. (6) Colour. (7) Electric Conductivity. (8) Conductivity. (9) Assay. (10) Ductility. (11) Physical Form.

Commercial silver solders are not known by their alloy percentages as with soft solders, but usually by a trade name or a number, such as "Melt-esi," "Easy-flo," or "G6," or by a British Standard Specification number. In any case, modern silver solders are not simple two-metal alloys, many of them being variations of a silver-copper-zinc-cadmium series of alloys. Details of hard solders manufactured by Johnson, Matthey & Co., Ltd., are shown in Table No. 2.

Silver solders are so much stronger and more ductile than soft solders, that they are often used to butt joint a sheet of metal, and afterward cold work, or 'raise' it, without detriment ; a process often used by copper and silversmiths. Some solders, it will be noted, have almost the same melting point, but different plastic range ; and this is sometimes useful if it is necessary to solder joints with greater than recommended clearance, the solders being used at a temperature slightly below the liquidous point so that the solder does not run so freely.

The recommended clearances for joints being hard soldered are somewhat less than those required for soft soldering, the former ranging from 0.001 to 0.003 in., and if clearances larger than these have to be joined then the method mentioned above must be used.

The fact that silver solders are available having melting points differing by 50 or 100 degrees is quite a useful property when a single article has more than one soldered joint, and a subsequent joint has to be made after the article has been worked on, because the first joint can be soldered using an alloy having a melting point well above that of the second solder to be used, and then there will be no fear of the first joint falling apart when the heat is applied to the second joint.

Silver soldered joints can be subject to working heats up to above 400° C., and brazed joints to far higher temperatures, depending on the alloy used.

Some hard solders and brazing strips, when used on copper, require no flux, such as "Silfos," "Silbralloy," and "Sifcupron," the first two being products of Johnson Matthew & Co., Ltd., and the last that of Suffolk Iron Foundries, Ltd., but these alloys should not be used on ferrous metals because there is a chance of brittle joints being formed.

Plain copper is one of the best brazing materials for joining ferrous metals, the strength of the joint often being higher than that of the metals being joined, if the clearances are small, say around 0.0002in. ; this is because an alloy forms right through the joint. Copper will also run into joints with very fine clearance and when they are of the order of 0.001 in. it will sometimes be drawn in as far as 5 or 6 inches by capillary attraction, whereas most brasses will not be drawn in more than $\frac{3}{4}$in. or so. The heat required to braze large pieces is very considerable when copper is used and oxy-acetylene is usually necessary, a temperature of about 1,110° C. being required.

Like soft solders, pre-placed discs, rings and cut-outs of hard solder can be used, and be placed in positions that would be quite inaccessible after assembly.

If the above variety of hard solders confounds the beginner let his choice be a low melting point solder like "Easy-flo" for hard soldering brass, or making joints that have to be cold worked. For joining copper or ferrous materials use a 50/50 brazing strip, or plain copper for steels if the necessary heat is available. It may be that the heat is not available even for 50/50 brasses, and then all hard soldering will have to carried out with silver solder with the added expense.

Silver solders can usually be supplied in the following physical forms: —

Rods, 24in. long, 3/16in., $\frac{1}{8}$in.; 12, 14 and 16 S.W.G.
Wire in coils from 1/16in. to 0.02in. dia.
Cut strips, 3/16in. x 0.04in., $\frac{1}{8}$in. x 0.04in., 1/16in. x 0.04in.
Foil, 0.005in. x 3in. wide.

CHAPTER 3

FLUXES

EXCEPT in one or two instances, fluxes are required when soldering or brazing. Although the oxide skin, which exists on the surface of metals exposed to the atmosphere, can be removed by mechanical abrasion, it starts to reform immediately, although it may not be apparent to the eye; however, it is sufficient to prevent the solder from making intimate contact with the metal and properly wetting or tinning it.

To overcome this, a flux is used, and this can be applied to the metals as a solid, a liquid, or a vapour; in the form of resin, zinc chloride, or ammonium chloride, to mention but a few. The action of a liquid flux is as follows:—The flux covers the metallic oxide skin and when heated boils and dissolves this skin on both the metal and the solder itself. The solder then moves forward on the oxide free metal, properly tinning it, in much the same way as two carpets can replace each other by rolling up one, and unrolling the other, without exposing the bare floor.

A good flux should possess the following properties: (1) It should have a solvent action on oxides; (2) be fluid at soldering temperatures; (3) be capable of being displaced by the solder; (4) be inexpensive; (5) be simple to apply; (6) leave a residue that is non-hygroscopic and not sticky; (7) have a residue that has a high electrical resistance; (8) be non-corrosive; (9) be highly active.

The manufacture of fluxes has become a specialized business and the owners of small workshops would be advised to purchase their fluxes ready made. As an indication of the different types of fluxes available commercially, the following is a list of products manufactured under the trade name

of "Baker's" soldering fluxes, which are one of the best
known: —

"Baker's" fluid for No. 1, for iron and steel.
    ,,   ,,   ,, No. 2, for brass and bronze.
    ,,   ,,   ,, No. 3, for copper and tinned metals.
    ,,   ,,   ,, F.A., for stainless steel and chromium.
    ,,   ,,   ,, F.B., for galvanized iron and zinc.
    ,,   ,,   ,, C.I., for cast iron.
    ,,   ,,   ,, C., for cadmium.
    ,,   ,,   ,, D.T.D.81 and 599.
    ,,   ,,   ,, Burnax Non-corrosive.
   ,, Soldering salts No. 1 for floating on solder or zinc
                           dipping baths.
   ,,   ,,   ,, No. 3, for soldering machines.
   ,, Soldering paste.
   ,, Tinning and soldering powder.

Actually No. 1 will cope with practically all types of work,
but the special fluxes may be either slightly quicker, cheaper,
or less corrosive.

However, as a matter of interest, a number of the recipes
for fluxes are given below.

Zinc Chloride (killed spirit).—Before proprietary fluxes
came into general use, killed spirit was the 'stand by' flux
of most workshops. It is made by dissolving as much zinc
as possible in a quantity of hydrochloric acid (Spirit of
salts). This should be done in a stone jar out in the open
air, because considerable amounts' of fumes are given off.
A second method is to dissolve in water fused zinc chloride
crystals—6oz. to 1 pint. This flux has a high melting point,
sometimes above that of the solder being used, and there
is a danger of weak joints caused by flux inclusions. This
may be overcome by adding 10% of ammonium chloride
which lowers the melting point of the flux. It may be
asked, how does a liquid flux melt? It will be noticed

when the flux is heated that it first dries, leaving a residue that is solid zinc chloride, and it is this which melts at 262° C. If the solder being used has a lower melting point than this, the solid flux will be trapped in the solder when it freezes, thus weakening the joint.

The above fluxes are very active but are also very corrosive and hygroscopic, and should be removed by washing in acidulated water, followed by hot water containing washing soda. The spray from this type of flux sometimes causes irritation of the skin and this can be neutralized by applying a weak solution of common washing soda ; and should any get into the eye, the eye should be bathed in a weak solution of bicarbonate of soda, using an eye bath.

Ammonium Chloride is not so effective as zinc chloride, but it is just as corrosive. When the flux cannot be washed away after the joint has been made, it is advisable to use a non-corrosive flux and the best known of these is : —

Rosin, Resin or Colophony. This is a gum, and it can be obtained in a number of grades. It melts at 80° C., and can be applied either as a powder, or as a liquid made by dissolving one part of resin in four parts of methylated spirit, or carbon tetrachloride ; the latter being preferred because it does not possess the fire hazard of the former. Although the danger of corrosion with a resin fluxed joint is absent, the joint is not quite so easy to make and more care is required. But even to-day, when non-corrosive activated resin fluxes are available, plain resin dissolved in ethyl-alcohol is used by those who want a flux that is above suspicion when soldering very fine wires.

Resin fluxes can be made more active by the addition of one part lactic acid to four parts resin, but this addition makes the flux slightly corrosive.

A number of commercial non-corrosive fluxes are available. Small amounts of organic activating substances are added to resin. Some of these are corrosive by themselves or are either neutralised by the heat or are present in carefully controlled proportions, so that no corrosive action takes place in the residue.

Tallow is another non-corrosive flux that is used mostly by plumbers when working with lead, but it protects the already clean metal from oxidization rather than dissolves the oxide skin.

Palm Oil is also a protective flux.

Paste Fluxes have the advantage that they remain where they are placed, and also can be manufactured as a core to wire solder, so that the current amount of solder is applied to the job. Such a paste can be made by mixing the following:—Petroleum jelly 6 parts, ammonium chloride 0.4 parts, zinc chloride 2.5 parts, water 0.75 parts. A liquid flux mixed with very finely powdered solder forms what is called a solder paint that can be painted on to the joint when cold, and is self tinning.

Very active fluxes in powder form are available that can be used to tin even rusty metal.

Although it is often possible to get results on various metals using but one flux, if a number of articles have to be soldered it is often more economical to purchase a flux made specially to suit that material or, if you wish to compound them yourself, make them up as follows for soft solders:—

For Stainless Steel.—Hydrochloric acid 1 part, zinc chloride 1 part.

For Cast Iron.—Zinc Chloride 15 parts, sodium chloride 3 parts, ammonium chloride 2 parts.

Aluminium Bronze and Silicon Bronze.—Hydrochloric acid 1 part, zinc chloride 1 part, water 4 parts.

Zinc Base Die Castings.—Use special solder or flux as given on page 63. Rub vigorously.

Aluminium.—Usually no flux is used but mechanical action during the soldering, or the oxide is broken up by supersonic vibration. Further information is given later.

When deciding which flux to use, use the most active providing after treatment allows the corrosive residue to be removed, otherwise use a non-corrosive one.

For hard soldering and brazing, borax ruled the roost for many years, sometimes 'nursed' with boric acid, and both these are still used for high melting point hard solders and for brazing strip, together with fluoborate fluxes; but for solders melting at temperatures below 750° C. fluxes with a lower melting point must be used, such as fluoride type fluxes or, better still, the special fluxes recommended by the makers of the hard solders being used.

If borax is used with a low melting point solder there is a real danger that the flux will solidify before the solder, and will be trapped in the joint, weakening it. Furthermore, borax residue is difficult to remove, whereas many of the proprietary fluxes can be removed by merely soaking the article in water.

When using these fluxes they are apt to boil up when heated while the water of crystalization is being driven off and displace any light parts or preplaced pieces of solder. This difficulty can be overcome with borax by melting it on a piece of polished steel, then scraping it off when cool, crushing it to a powder and then mixing it with water to form a milky liquid. Manufacturing jewellers use the same thing in lump form and it is called calcined borax. A lump about the size of a small potato is rubbed down as required on a small slab of slate that has had a few drops of water sprinkled on to it, and the milky liquid applied to the article with a small camel hair brush

CHAPTER 4

HEATING DEVICES

THE heating of the solder, and the metals to be joined, can be carried out by a number of different methods, the principal ones being as follows: —(1) By means of a heated soldering iron; (2) By flame; (3) By dipping; (4) By high frequency induction; (5) By ovens; (6) By local resistance heating.

Soldering Irons.—These could be more truthfully called soldering coppers, because the bit is made from a short length of copper bar, which is usually shaped to a point and is joined to a wooden handle by a length of steel rod, as shown in Fig. 4. Other metals could be used for the bit, but it has been found that copper is the most suitable for a number of reasons. The weight of the bit is important: it should be appropriate to the work being tackled; that is to say, it should be as light as possible, so that it does not tire the worker but must be of such a size that the heat is not drained away from the bit before the joint can be made properly.

The ideal size is one that will not require continual re-heats and yet will not tire the operator unduly. For 'every-day' work a 6-ounce bit is a good all-round size, but for soldering tin-lined packing cases, an iron three or four times this size might not be found too large. On the other hand, for soldering joints in radio sets, a 2 or 3 ounce bit would most likely fill the bill because, being slimmer, it could be manoeuvred more easily amongst the close wiring. Many workers make their own irons, often to a special shape to suit the work in hand, and a drawing of two such irons are shown in Fig. 5. These irons weigh less than half an

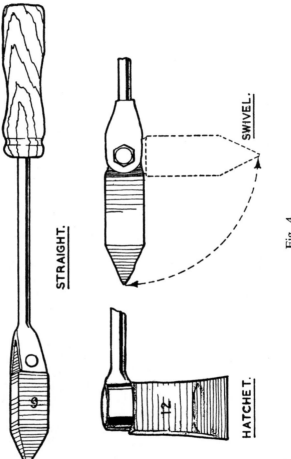

STRAIGHT.

SWIVEL.

HATCHET.

Fig. 4

ounce, and they are both used by different operatives to carry out the same job—soldering bronze hair-springs on electrical measuring instruments. For sealing the packing cases mentioned above, the hatchet shaped iron is a useful instrument. A. H. Wilkes & Co., Ltd., make soldering irons in weights from 2oz. to 64oz., from electrolytic rolled and drawn copper.

Bits slowly lose their shape through continual filing and cleaning, and they should then be reshaped by bringing them to a red heat and forging them with a hammer on an anvil; they are then reheated and quenched to obtain a fine grain structure.

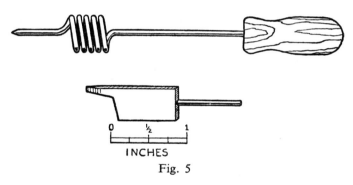

INCHES

Fig. 5

All these types of soldering irons require some means of heating them, and the usual method is to use a special Bunsen burner, or a gas fired soldering iron furnace, as shown in Fig. 6, or by an electrical muffle furnace. For the occasional job, the iron can be heated over an ordinary gas ring, but in the type of furnace mentioned above the flame does not come in direct contact with the iron: it heats a small hollow fire brick which in turn heats the iron by radiant heat and this reduces the oxidization and therefore the frequency of cleaning and tinning of the bit.

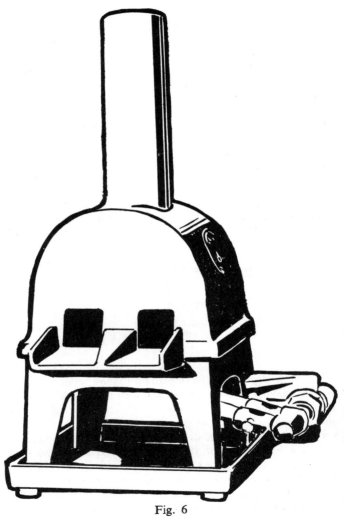

Fig. 6

Plate No. 5. High frequency induction heater. The single turn water-cooled heating coil can be seen on the front below the instruments

Plate No. 6. High frequency induction soldering size studs to the back of a bonnet louvre at one operation. Heating time 18 seconds.

Plate No. 7. Home-made low pressure gas torch, making use of standard Keith Blackman 3/4" injector

Plate No. 8. The "Flamemaster" Hand Torch with accessories

From left to rig
Oxy-air mixer (
Flexiflame Jet (
Soldering-bolt (
Nozzle-cap for
with F, KLM
Maxiflame unit
(TU)
Standard Torch
(ABDTU)
Gas/oxy Jets
(KLM)
Double-tipping
attachment (Q c

The electric muffle is usually more expensive but can be thermostatically controlled more easily.

The iron can, of course, be heated by paraffin blow lamp, and this is the method usually used when soldering has to be done away from the workshop and no electricity is available. The lamp itself can be made part of the iron and a number of manufacturers make such an iron: or bottled petroleum gas can be used, and in this case a gas soldering iron should be used, and these are available both for use with town gas and petroleum gas. See Fig. 7.

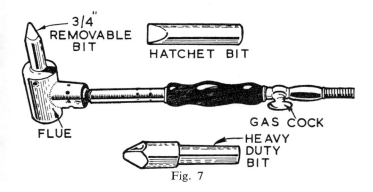

Fig. 7

To-day, however, the electric iron is the one used for most continuous soldering jobs; they can be obtained in a number of weights and wattages, from about 10 to 250 watts and voltages from 6 to 250.

A number of these irons can be obtained with interchangeable bits, and most of them with renewable elements. A selection of such irons is shown in Plate No. I. The Wolf Electric Tool Co., Ltd., manufacture an iron that has an automatic feed for the solder and this is illustrated in Plate No. II. A reel of cored solder is supported on the back of the iron and the correct amount of solder fed to the tip of the iron by pressure on a trigger. A type of special soldering iron that is becoming very popular is the pencil type, and, as its name implies, it is about the size and shape of a pencil and is extremely useful when joints have to be made in close proximity to each other, as in radio work. A further advantage is that they heat up very quickly, some of them within 60 seconds, as against 5 to 10 minutes with the ordinary type. They cannot, of course, be used for heavy work, the bit being much too light. They are manufactured by a number of firms. One is shown in Plate No. III. Still smaller ones are available for instrument work and by manufacturers of hearing aids.

Soldering of aluminium has always been a problem, but Mullards, Ltd., have now produced a supersonic soldering iron which breaks up the oxide skin as quickly as it forms by means of supersonic vibrations. The bit is heated by the normal means but it is also vibrated by a coil through which passes an alternating current at an ultrasonic frequency: this vibration completely destroys the oxide skin, allowing the metal to be completely tinned. This method can be used on metal other than aluminium. See Plate No. IV. A supersonic tinning bath is also available.

The copper bit of soldering irons should never be allowed to overheat whatever type is used. If, with flame-heated irons, the flame burns green then the iron is being overheated; a rough intimation of the correct heat is that it should just scorch paper in 4 to 5 seconds. Overheating causes excessive oxidization, pitting, and burning of the solder, necessitating continual cleaning and tinning. To overcome this, the iron when hot should not be placed completely in the flame but only so that the flame may brush the rear part of it. With electrical soldering irons the tip of the bit should rest on a piece of metal to draw off the surplus heat.

It must be remembered that the electric iron, for a given

weight of bit, is always heavier than a plain iron, and added
to this is the pull of the flex which prevents that full freedom
of movement obtainable with the plain iron; these points
must be considered when deciding which to use.

For sweating, a Bunsen burner working at atmospheric
pressure is usually sufficient in the small workshop, and for
small batches of dipped work a plumber's ladle, or gas-
heated plumber's pot is often used; but for large quantities
thermostatically controlled dipping baths are needed.

High frequency heaters are only to be found in shops
dealing with the mass production work, for which they are
in some cases ideal. The method of operation is roughly
as follows:—A high frequency current in the neighbour-
hood of one megacycle is generated and passed through a
water-cooled coil; the article to be soldered is placed
within the coil and heated by induction in a very short
time, often only a matter of a few seconds. Some steels
heat quicker than others, and much faster than copper or

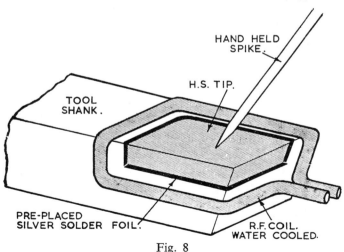

HAND HELD
SPIKE.

H.S. TIP.

TOOL
SHANK.

PRE-PLACED
SILVER SOLDER FOIL.

R.F. COIL.
WATER COOLED.

Fig. 8

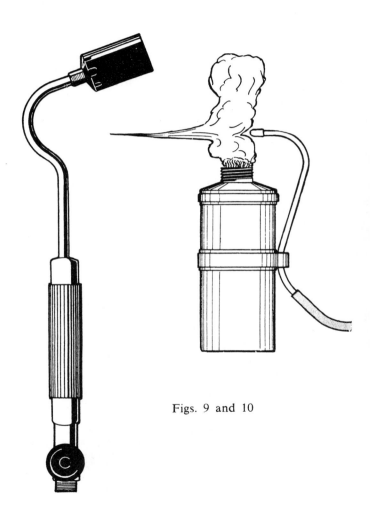

Figs. 9 and 10

brass. The solder can be preplaced, and the articles passed through the coil on a conveyor belt. The method is ideal for soft, or silver soldering a large number of small articles. Such an apparatus is shown in Plate V and VI and Fig. 8 shows the coil shaped to surround the end of a lathe tool being tipped with high speed steel.

Hard soldering is invariably carried out by means of a torch of some kind, in a muffle furnace, or in an open hearth (the latter method being seldom used now) or, as previously mentioned, by high frequency induction.

The torches used vary greatly. from the small methylated blowlamp shown in Fig. 9 to the acetylene blow torch made by the British Oxygen Co., Ltd., and shown in Fig. 10. In between these there is the ordinary paraffin blowlamp in various sizes (Fig. 11), but for brazing anything of any size like a small model locomotive boiler say 3in. diameter and 15in. long, a six pint lamp is required at least.

Coal gas torches can be divided into three main categories: the atmospheric or self blowing, those requiring compressed air, and oxy-coal gas blow pipes that use gas at town pressures and compressed oxygen.

The small self blowing torch like the "Davi-jet" is extremely useful for jewellery and for silver soldering small jobs up to, say, joining two pieces of mild steel $\frac{1}{8}$in. x 1/16in. Above this size there are a number of self blowing blow pipes on the market; or a very efficient one can be made by using a Keith-Blackman atmospheric injector, as shown in Plate No. VII. If used without an extension pipe the flame is about as fierce as one can get without pressurized air, or almost so. They are comparitively cheap and can easily have a handle attached to them as shown. The smallest size made is $\frac{1}{2}$in., which refers to the size of the barrel for which the outlet is screwed. About the largest size that can be used off the normal domestic supply is $\frac{3}{4}$in. With the $\frac{1}{2}$in. size it is just about possible to silver solder two pieces of ⅛in. x ½in., mild steel together, using a low melting point solder, say not above 650° C.

The plain mouth blow pipe used in conjunction with a small coal gas flame or methylated spirit lamp is ideal for soldering very small articles, such as a clip on to an ear ring, and these are extensively used by jewellers and dental mechanics.

Remember, however, that it is not only the temperature of the flame that matters, but also the amount of heat

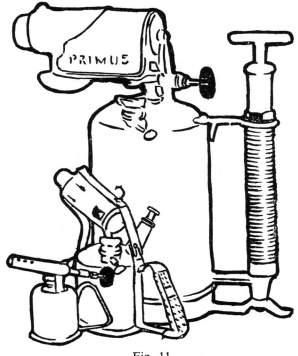

Fig. 11

available; it must be supplied faster than it can be conducted away.

The jeweller often prefers the French blow pipe, Fig. 12. This pipe is held in the hand and has a finger control for the gas supply, the air being blown from the mouth. The use of this type of mouth blowpipe means that only one hand is left to hold the work and so it is that some other workers in precious metals prefer a pipe fixed to the bench and a very useful one is that designed by Mr. L. B. Woodward, of the L.C.C. Central School of Arts and Crafts, which is shown in Fig. 13. The plain gas burner is screwed to the bench by its flange and then three or four turns of copper pipe ⅛in. diameter are wound round it and the end, having been tapered down to form a fine jet, is adjusted to come over the outlet, the other end of the tube being connected to a rubber pipe and a mouthpiece.

To carry out brazing on any article larger than ¼in.

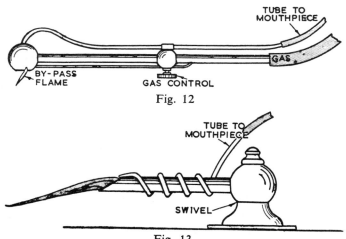

Fig. 12

Fig. 13

square, using 50/50 brazing strip, requires a pressurized air supply, or acetylene.

A very simple but efficient blow pipe is shown in Fig. 13a and is made by Fletcher Russell & Co., Ltd. They make this pattern with or without tape for controlling the gas and air supply.

Fig. 13a

An extremely useful torch is the Chance "Flamemaster" (Plate No. VIII). This can be fitted with a number of jets, and even with the one type of jet it is possible to obtain quite a large brazing flame using 8 cubic ft. gas per hour to a needle-like flame useful for jewellery work. By changing the nozzle a larger flame can be obtained, using up to 30 cubic feet of gas per hour with gas pressures of 11in. water glass and air pressure of 3-10lb. With still a further type of jet oxygen at 20lb. pressure can be used, and cutting and light alloy welding carried out; butane with oxygen can also be used.

It must be realized that it is not the size of the flame that counts so much as the intensity. Plate No. IX shows a flame from the jet of a torch with, and without, an addition of pressurized air, and it will be seen that one is very much smaller than the other, although both are consuming the same quantity of gas and giving off the same amount of heat. But it is obvious that one of them is giving it off in a much smaller volume, and the flame will therefore be much hotter. The flame becomes smaller because when compressed air is mixed with the gas, oxygen is supplied to the coal gas with greater speed, allowing the gas to burn quicker. It can be made to burn still faster by mixing it with compressed oxygen. When the oxygen is supplied in the form of air it is, of course, mixed with nitrogen which does not help the combustion in any way but does, in fact, reduce the heat of the flame because some of the heat is used to raise the temperature of this nitrogen and is carried off with it. If still higher temperatures are required air-acetylene torches are available, using from about 2 to 15 cubic feet of acetylene per hour.

It must be remembered that the size of the flame is no indication of what the torch is capable of doing, because with small objects a lot of the heat would be wasted by the fact that some of the flame would not strike the article being brazed, and further, the heat may be transferred so slowly to the article that it might be conducted away more quickly than it is applied. This is the secret of oxy-acetylene welding; the small flame transfers the heat so quickly that little can leak away before the metal reaches fusing point.

For brazing any articles of greater cross section area than $\frac{1}{4}$in., using 50/50 brazing strip, a compressed air torch is almost a necessity and then the method of compressing the air has to be considered. For the usual type of blow pipe, pressures of 1lb. and about 2 cubic feet a minute are required; these quantities can be supplied by a foot bellows (see Fig. 14). For higher pressures a mechanical rotary blower will be necessary (Fig. 15). These can be obtained in numerous sizes, directly coupled to a motor or fitted with a pulley for belt drive. An ordinary piston-type compressor can be used, but the blow-off valve must be set at a very low pressure or, if this is not possible, a reducing valve should be used.

Details of some of the flame temperatures obtainable are shown in Table No. 3. These are only approximate, because there are a number of variables when the gases are used outside the laboratory, but will act as a guide to the reader who has to decide what equipment to purchase.

TABLE No. 3

Atmospheric air and coal gas	1,400 centigrade
Compressed air and coal gas	1,700 ,,
Compressed air and propane	1,850 ,,
Compressed air and butane	1,900 ,,
Compressed oxygen and coal gas	2,100 ,,
Compressed air and acetylene	2,400 ,,
Compressed oxygen and propane	2,600 ,,
Compressed oxygen and butane	3,000 ,,
Compressed oxygen and acetylene	3,200 ,,

The approximate volumes of different gas required to give the same amount of heat are shown below in Table No. 4. The second column indicates the comparative costs of the gases in pence per cubic foot.

TABLE No. 4

Acetylene	1 cubic foot	1.6 pence
Coal gas	4 cubic feet	0.075 ,,
Propane	0.85 cubic feet	0.8 ,,
Oxygen	—	0.3 ,,

Although certain torches and blowlamps are advertised as being suitable for using with more than one type of gas, it will usually be found that far better results are obtainable if a torch designed for that specific gas is used.

Cylinders of gas are usually hired out or loaned free to the users of large quantities of gas, but the suppliers are understandably reluctant to hire out the cylinders to very small users, and at present there is a great shortage of them.

The hottest part of a flame can easily be found by playing it on a piece of coke and noticing the difference in brilliance; it will then be apparent that the hottest part is at the tip of the blue-violet cone, but this portion of the flame is

Fig. 14

usually made up of reducing gases, and these are easily assimilated by the molten solder which, upon solidifying, gives up this gas which causes porosity of the joint. It is therefore advisable to use the envelope of the flame (see Fig. 16), at least whilst the solder is molten.

The flame should be just oxidising for preference, that is to say, it should be a bushy type of flame, but certainly showing no yellow. A fiercer flame might be hotter but it may also oxidize too much. Experience only can tell you.

A vast difference in the size of the article that can be brazed with a given size of flame can be made if due consideration is given to the lagging of the article by binding it with asbestos cloth or tape, or burying it all except

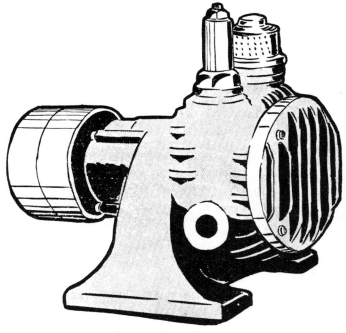

Fig. 15

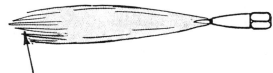

USE THIS PORTION
OF THE FLAME.

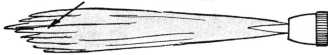

Fig. 16

the portion being heated, in small coke (as shown in frontispiece) ; in this latter case considerable help can be obtained
from the glowing coke itself if the flame is occasionally
played onto it. Heat may also be conserved by using fire
bricks to reflect it or, in the case of small repetition work,
arranging the articles on a tray in such a manner that the
waste heat impinges on the next article to be soldered or
brazed.

Further methods of supplying the necessary heat for
brazing are the high frequency induction method—already
referred to in soft soldering—and the resistance heating
method. The latter consists of passing a large current
through a carbon electrode in contact with the work,
heating this electrode which, in turn, heats the work—very
locally—by conduction. This current is usually supplied
from a step down transformer tapped to give output voltages
of 2, 3, 4, and 5 volts, and currents up to 250 amps.
One lead from the transformer goes to the electrode holder,
the other being clipped to the work. As one portion of the
work heats up to the required temperature the electrode is
slowly moved along the joint. Sheet metals, up to about
16 S.W.G., can be joined by this method and a number of
commercial equipments are on the market. The main
advantage of this method of brazing is the extremely local
heating. (See Plate, No. IX.)

Hearths.—Some kind of hearth is required for both soft
and hard soldering, but for the former a sheet of asbestos
mill-board is all that is required. It should be noted that
metal, or even a firebrick, should not be used because these
materials are likely to conduct the heat away too quickly.

The jeweller uses either charcoal block or a wire 'wig'
for a hearth. The latter article is a pancake of compressed
iron wire squeezed flat, so that it is about six inches in
diameter and about one inch thick, and usually mounted
on a wooden handle.

The silversmith and model engineer requires something larger than this, but it may be quite simple, such as a cut-down oil-drum or an old bucket filled with coke or asbestos cubes. Preferably it should have a back shield of iron or fire brick ; it is an advantage if it can be revolved, and has some kind of clamp supported from the back. A very useful type of hearth is one built up of firebricks that can be purchased from any ironmonger for domestic use.

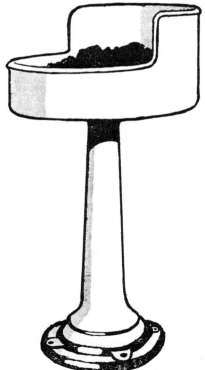

Fig. 17

A professional type of hearth is shown in Fig. 17 and is a type manufactured by Fletcher Russell & Co., Ltd.

If considerable work is to be carried out it is advisable to have a hood and vent over the hearth to carry away the fumes, especially if much coal gas is to be burnt, because the by-products of such a form of heat contain considerable water vapour, and if the fumes are not extracted from the workshop they will cause considerable trouble from rust.

It is essential, if the torch has no cut-off when laid aside, that a safe suspension hook is arranged, otherwise a fire will soon be started accidentally.

When a number of small articles are to be soldered together, it is sometimes found difficult to support them, and this difficulty can often be overcome by using plasticine if the portion to be soldered is not too close: for instance, if it is required to solder some wire to form miniature tubular furniture. If the joint will be so close to the plasticine that the heat will melt it then plaster of paris can be used, this material being especially useful when silver soldering jewellery, etc., but the mixture should be weakened by mixing silver sand with it—three of sand to one of plaster— so that it may afterwards be easily broken away from the work. Dentists use what they term "mud", this is very wet moulding sand, or silver sand mixed with 10% Fullers earth. The articles are first stuck together with sticky wax—50/50 beeswax and paraffin wax, and then the extremities are buried in the mud.

Readers are reminded that they are legally required to fit a non-return valve to their town gas supply, if they connect any form of air or gas supply under pressure to these mains.

* Further notes on types of soldering irons, see author's note, page 86.

Chapter 5

SOFT SOLDERING

The first job to do if you are using a new soldering iron is to tin it. This operation is often mentioned as if it was the most difficult operation in the world, whereas really it is one of the simplest, and can be carried out successfully in a number of ways, such as the following:—Heat the iron just sufficiently to melt the solder (if it is giving out a green flame it is too hot), remove from the flame and file the tip clean but only that portion necessary to do the job, because some irons are sherardized to prevent the untinned portion oxidizing. Now do *one* of the following:—

(*a*) On a piece of tin plate—the top of a cocoa tin will do—dab some flux; place the end of a stick of blow pipe solder on the flux and the hot iron on the end of the solder; melt a small blob on to the tin plate and then rub the iron into it, and the iron should immediately take a coating of solder.

(*b*) Clean the tip of the iron and apply the end of some cored solder to it.

(*c*) Dip the end of a stick of blow pipe solder in to the flux and apply to the end of the cleaned iron.

If the tip fails to tin successfully, it is almost certain to be because the iron has been overheated. If, when the copper bit is filed, the bright copper immediately is covered with a dark layer of oxide instead of this action taking a number of seconds, then the iron is too hot. If you are using paste or liquid flux it is a safeguard to dip the tip of the iron in the flux immediately after filing it and then at once carry out the other procedure. It should be mentioned here that care should be taken when dipping an electric iron into liquid

Plate No. 9. Copy of photograph showing size of gas flame with and without the addition of pressurized air, both flames consuming the same quantity of gas.

Plate No. 10. Brazing by resistance heating

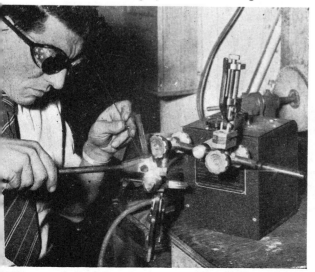

Plate No. 11. Soldering a patch on the bottom of a kettle

flux that only the tip of the bit enters the flux, otherwise there is a danger of the liquid entering the heating element and destroying it, or at least causing an electrical short. It would be as well to note at the same time that a proper three-pin plug is joined to a three-wire lead so that the iron is safely earthed, otherwise it can be a great danger to the user, unless a low voltage iron and transformer are used. This latter method allows for the use of a very flexible and light lead.

The soldering iron is often used to carry the solder to the joint, and it is often important that a minimum of solder should be used for the joint, as in electrical instrument work. In such cases only sufficient of the bit should be tinned to carry the necessary solder. It will be found that if the iron is overheated after tinning, the solder on it will become burnt and it will have to be re-tinned. All the time the molten solder is lying on the tip of the bit it is gradually dissolving the copper away, and after a considerable number of hours' use, the bit will become badly pitted and require filing and re-tinning. The bit often picks up dirt whilst being used and it is as well to have a piece of cloth or carpet near by on which to rub the tip of the iron. A suggested cycle of operations for soldering would be as follows: having tinned the iron, remove iron from flame, dip tip into flux, wipe tip on cloth, and then apply to the job with the solder. Don't use the leg of your overalls to wipe the iron on, because you will eventually find you are wiping it on your bare leg!

The beginner is advised to carry out a few experiments on some scrap brass and mild steel before tackling a proper job. Try the effects of flux on different types of metal; try cleaning, partially cleaning, and leaving dirty the metal to be soldered and note the effect. By the way, most text books tell you to be certain that the metal is free from oil and grease, but the danger of the oil is not that it prevents the soldering of clean metal but prevents the flux reaching unclean metal. If a piece of brass is cleaned carefully and then smeared with machine oil it will be found that the brass can still be tinned if the iron is rubbed on it for a second or two.

Note how the solder spreads out over a really clean and well-fluxed piece of metal, or runs into the joint spaces between two metals.

A very simple practical soldering job would be to join two 20 S.W.G. bare copper wires together. First carefully clean the ends of the wires for a length of an inch, either by scraping or by rubbing it with sand-paper (sand-paper is preferred to emery paper for this job), twist half an inch of one wire—not on to the other but into the other, so that when twisted the twist is parallel to the wire (see Fig. 18). Now paint with flux, melt a blob of solder on to the tip of the iron and apply this to the twisted portion of the wires,

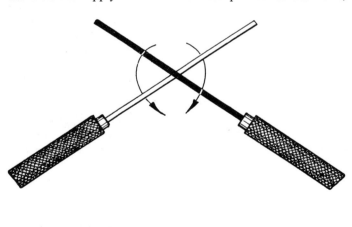

Fig. 18

and leave it there for a second or two. The solder should now run along the whole length of the twisted portion, although this will depend to a certain extent on the quality of solder being used; 50/50 will run more easily along the wire than 40/60 and it is therefore as well to rub the tip of the iron along the twisted portion just to make sure of things. If the solder being used was of the cored type, then the procedure would be slightly different, because no separate flux is used in this case, but the tip of the solder is placed on the twisted wire, and the point of the iron placed on this so that the flux is first melted out of the solder and then runs along the wire, immediately followed by the molten solder.

When connecting up radio and similar work, it is the usual practice to take one turn of the wire round the tag before soldering it. This not only holds the wire in place whilst the job is being done but also strengthens the joint. However, when an experimental job is being done it is not advisable to make a twisted joint because some difficulty may be experienced at a later date when an alteration to a connection has to be made, and these alterations are often many.

In such a case it is as well just to lay the end of the wire on to the tag and then solder it. Now that is more easily said than done, because this usually means that you want three hands—one to hold the wire in place, one to hold the cored solder, and one to hold the iron. There are alternatives and the simplest is to use a separate flux ; or the wire and the tag can be tinned separately and then brought together, or held in position with the iron and the solder applied, and the wire then held by the tip of a screwdriver until the solder has set; or the wire may be just hooked under the tag. With small assemblies the iron can be held in a clamp or vice and the job brought to it.

Some small radio components are extremely delicate and sensitive to heat, and this is another reason why a low melting point solder should be used, say 60/40. In special cases the heat conduction can be reduced by clipping over the wire a spring clip with heavy copper jaws, or by pushing the connecting wire of the component through a slice of potato that is afterwards removed; but this is only a makeshift.

It is important that only non-corrosive, non-conductive, non-hygroscopic fluxes be used for radio and similar work. For close work of this kind the pencil type of soldering iron will be found extremely helpful, and even lighter types, weighing only an ounce or two complete, are now available as electric irons for instrument and hearing-aid work.

In radio work two faults must be watched for: the first, dry joints which are extremely difficult to spot, but can cause crackling. These are usually caused by imperfect tinning, the joint being held in position by an interlocking of the solder with the tag and the wire, usually caused by bad fluxing or insufficient heat—not necessarily in the iron but because the joint was made too quickly. A second point to watch is the dropping of blobs of solder amongst the components. Find it at once if you notice it drop. It may save you countless hours later when you have forgotten exactly where you dropped it or, worse still, the destruction of some expensive component by a 'short.' The solder recommended for experimental radio work is non-corrosive cored 60/40 tin-lead. It is rather expensive, and the next best is 50/50 ; but if you cannot get or cannot afford the high tin solders, it must be admitted that the vast majority of commercial work is carried out with cored solder of the 40/60 alloy. Make certain the cored flux is non-corrosive— both types are sold.

A slightly more difficult soldering job is putting a patch on the bottom of an iron kettle, and the chief difficulty here is getting the spot really clean. If it is a copper kettle, perhaps the easiest way is to scrape the spot with a knife, but with a tinned steel or iron kettle things are not quite so easy, because the surrounding metal is most likely badly pitted with rust and in that case wire brushing, scraping, and rubbing with emery cloth may all be required. If, say, the hole is a small one, about 1/16in., then an area of about one inch diameter should be cleaned round it and when perfectly clean it may be fluxed (Plate XI, No. 1), preferably with a corrosive one, because they make tinning easier. Paint on liquid flux with the crushed end of a soft wood stick, or a Jeweller's glass brush. The spot is then tinned by melting a spot of solder on to the cleaned area (2), rubbing it in with the heated soldering iron. It may be found that the solder does not want to 'take' on the cleaned iron, in which case brush more flux on to the now heated area, and then rub in the solder again. Some sheet irons are extremely difficult to tin, but repeated applications of a corrosive flux to the hot metal usually does the job. Having successfully tinned the cleaned spot, a disc of metal of suitable thickness and material, say 22 S.W.G. copper or even thinner tinned plate, is cut slightly smaller than the cleaned area, is now also tinned which, being of clean material, should cause no difficulty. This tinned disc should now be placed over the hole and pressed on to it with the heated soldering iron (3), which should be moved around to melt the solder all over the patch, keeping as large an area of the iron as possible in contact with it. To prevent the disc sliding about, it can be held in position by the tip of a screwdriver. When the whole of the patch has been heated so that the solder is molten the iron is removed, but the patch is still held down until the solder solidifies. The kettle is now well swilled out and washed on the outside to remove any flux residue. For the above type of work a six ounce iron would be about the right size, and 40/60 solder the material to use, with, say, Baker's No. 1 flux.

Alternatively, the cleaned portion of the kettle and the

patch may be painted with solder paint and heated with the flame of a blow pipe (4) and when a bright ring of solder is seen round the disc it is pressed down with a damp rag (5), squeezing the surplus solder out of the joint and cooling it immediately.

To solder a lapped joint there is usually no need to tin the overlapping portions first, but they must be cleaned and fluxed; if the joint is of any length it will usually be found necessary to secure the two pieces in position in some way. This can best be done by clamping them at the ends of the joint with two toolmaker's clamps: the joint can then be tacked in position with blobs of solder. The clamps are now removed and, starting from one end, the joint is soldered by melting solder on the front of the iron and then slowly moving it forward; the molten solder will run between the joint by capillary attraction if properly heated.

It may be found that as the iron moves forward the metal springs apart before the solder has time to freeze, and if this happens the iron should be followed up by pressing the joint with a bar of metal, which will not only squeeze out the surplus metal but will immediately cool the joint and solidify the solder.

For soldering large tinned steel containers a still larger iron weighing anything up to three or four pounds may be required, and by some workers the hatchet-shaped iron is preferred and again the solder is fed to the front of the iron, and the surplus pushed forward.

When soldering folded joints this not only makes the joint watertight, but at the same time locks the joint so that there is no possibility of it coming apart.

A soldering job that often brings grief to the beginner is that of soldering a nipple on to a Bowden cable. The job is not too difficult if the cable is new, but when it is old, oily and dirty: then the trouble commences. If the cable has to be shortened, clean the cable as best you can with petrol without unravelling it and then try to get sufficient solder to adhere an inch below the place where the cut is to be made, so that it will stop the cable from unravelling, then cut it to length. Now unravel it for about half an inch and clean each individual strand—scraping is the best way—twist them together again, pass them through the nipple and then spread out the ends, flux and solder, and then clean off the end with a file.

If the cable is new it is usually only necessary to degrease it and then flux it, and solder the end to be cut before cutting it. The soldered end is then passed through the nipple and splayed out by nipping it in the vice or with pliers before soldering it to the nipple.

Actually the soldering iron is seldom used in the small workshop except for electrical work; most other jobs are carried out by sweating, that is to say, tinning both surfaces to be joined, placing them together and then heating them over a flame. The patch put on the kettle could easily have been done this way ; the area that had been cleaned would have been fluxed and then heated with a blow pipe or Bunsen burner, a blob of solder melted onto it from the stick, and the solder then brushed over the area with a glass brush, or rubbed in with the heated soldering iron, and the patch treated in the same way. The patch can now be laid on the hole in the kettle bottom and heated, and as soon as the solder is molten the heat is removed and the patch pressed down with a damp cloth which will freeze the solder and squeeze out any surplus. The use of a damp cloth for this purpose is only recommended for light articles, if used on heavy work there is a danger of scalding the hand from the large amount of steam formed.

A type of joint very often required in the small workshop is the soldering of various fittings onto pipes, nipples and flanges, etc. If the fit of these is less than 3 thous. the pipe and the fitting must be pre-tinned before threading one on the other, but if the clearance is between 3 thous. and up to 10 thous., then the joint can be treated as what is known as a "capillary" joint. With such a joint, the end of the pipe and the fitting are both cleaned with wire wool or glasspaper, see Plate No. XII (1), then fluxed, preferably with a paste flux (2), and the fitting placed in position ; the whole assembly is now heated with a blowlamp (3) and when hot enough the stick of solder is touched on the edge of the joint, and as it melts the solder will be drawn into joint space by capillary attraction, completely filling it. Some domestic water pipe fittings are specially manufactured for soldering in this manner, and in some cases the solder is even contained in a grove sunk on the inside of the fitting. This latter type of fitting is known as "The Yorkshire," as it is manufactured by the Yorkshire Copper Pipe Co. Ltd.

If, however, the clearances are below 3 thous., then the soft solders are not fluid enough to be drawn into such a fine space and, as previously mentioned, the fitting and pipe must be pre-tinned; to do this the pipe and fitting is first cleaned, then fluxed and heated, and a blob of solder melted on to the end of the pipe and the inside of the fitting. Wiping the end of the pipe with a piece of dry rag will usually spread the blob of solder and completely tin the pipe, or it can be painted with solder paint [(4) and (5)].

Large fittings can be treated in the same way, but nipples and the like below ½in. diameter are best tinned by using a small copper rod slightly less than the inside diameter of the nipple, or if the clearance is not too small the pipe can be pushed into the nipple, giving a turn and then withdrawn keeping the pipe and the nipple at the liquidus temperature; more solder is now added to the pipe, which is pushed back into the nipple and the job is done.

When installing a domestic water system using capillary

type of joint, it is the usual practice to assemble large portions of the total installation before soldering up any of the joints; this enables a check to be made that all is O.K. In order to protect paintwork from the heat of the blow lamp on this sort of job, place in front of it a damp asbestos cloth or mill board. Care should be taken when testing out such water systems that the joint is well and truly made, and that a leak is not hidden by solidified flux, and for this reason cold water systems should be tested under pressure and hot water systems tested under heat. Should a small leak occur on a hot water system when a secondary circuit is employed, it is often a simple matter to cure it by adding a pound of fine oatmeal to every twenty gallons of water in the circulating circuit. The most certain way of making a good joint in the capillary type of fitting when preplaced solder is not used, is to employ solder paint.

The preplaced solder mentioned in the last paragraph is a comparatively complicated method of preplacing it, and is carried out when the fitting is manufactured. A simpler way, but in some cases not such an effective way, is to use rings of solder wire. The rings can easily be made by winding core solder round a stick, removing the stick and then cutting through the resultant coil with tin snips lengthwise. This will turn the coil of solder into a quantity of separate rings. Plain solder wire can be used, but this will necessitate the pre-fluxing of the joint. Preplaced solder foil is a useful method of fixing a quantity of name plates.

Wiping a Joint. One of the oldest methods of joining two lead pipes, or a lead pipe to a copper or iron fitting is by means of a 'wiped' joint. It has been said that the secret of making a good wiped joint is plenty of solder, plenty of confidence, and plenty of practice.

In other words there is no trade secret about it—just plenty of skill. To make such a joint by the 'pot-wipe' method requires four or five pounds of plumber's solder at least—not all of which is used on the actual joint, of course —and this method has the advantage from the beginner's point of view that he is not so likely to melt the pipe itself as he might do if he used the blowlamp method. Whichever method is going to be used, the pipe must be prepared in the same way. Fig. 19 shows the special points to be noted and Plate No. XIII (1) shows actual pipes ready for wiping. The two pipe ends must first be shaped, one being rasped down to a spigot and the other opened out

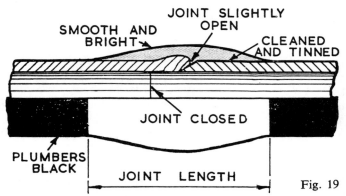

Fig. 19

to a socket by means of a 'turnpin'; or both ends may be shaped by means of a steel jointer. The end six inches of the pipes are now 'tarnished' or 'soiled,' which consists of painting the pipe with a mixture of glue size and lamp black or, if preferred, a proprietary brand may be used. To make the job look neat, a band of paper should be

wrapped round the pipe six inches from the end to mask
the pipe and form a neat boundary to the 'soiled' portion.
The exterior limits of the joint are now scraped clean on
the outside and also the inside portion of the socket.

Check up on the drawing of the joint, Fig. 19, and note
that the taper of the spigot should be about $\frac{1}{4}$in. to $\frac{3}{8}$in.
long; that the inside of the joint should be a close fit, so
that the solder cannot run into the pipe; that the outside
of the joint should be slightly open so that the solder can be
drawn into it by capillary attraction, and fill it; but this
clearance should be only small. As soon as the joint has
been soiled, and the joint surfaces cleaned, they should be
tallowed to prevent oxidization.

Now prepare a potful of plumber's solder, 30/70 type,
and heat it until a piece of paper dipped into the molten
solder for a couple of seconds turns a golden brown—if the
paper ignites the solder is too hot. The joint is now heated
by taking a ladle full of solder and dribbling it over the
joint. At first the solder will solidify on the pipe without
sticking to it but as more solder is dribbled on, the pipe
heats up and the solder remains pasty. A strip of moleskin
or fustian is now folded to form a six- or seven-inch square
'drip' cloth, and this is held below the joint, and as the
pasty mass slides off the pipe it is caught in this cloth and
pushed around the joint, thus tinning it, as shown in (2).
If the mass of solder does not appear molten enough to
run into the joint and tin it, this solder held in the 'drip'
cloth should be discarded and fresh solder poured over the
joint, caught in the 'drip' cloth and pushed around the
joint until it is properly tinned. The drip cloth is then
replaced by the smaller 'wiping pad'; this smaller pad is a
square of moleskin of such a size that the sides are the same
length as the joint, and it is a narrow strip of moleskin
wrapped round a piece of cardboard and then tallowed; the
rough side of the cloth can be inside or out, the choice

smooth finish to the wipe. The finishing end of the moleskin strip should be sewn to one edge. A little more solder
is now dribbled over the joint to warm it and the new
cloth, up: the mass of solder is then wiped round the
joint and moulded into the well-known shape. If the
location of the pipe allows it, the wipe should be made in
one complete sweep round the joint, and about three sweeps
are usually necessary to mould the joint nicely; the final
sweep is made using both hands to bend the pad to a
nice shape and bring pressure on the edges to clean them
up (3). The resultant seam of solder at the end of the
final sweep is removed by means of a small piece of moleskin called a 'drag off.' This is a strip of cloth about half
an inch wide and the seam of solder is dragged off in a
direction parallel to the pipes. On no account should
the solder be manipulated after it has cooled to a chalky
white appearance, but only whilst it has a metallic gleam.
In order to guard against porous joints, it should be wiped
over with tallow as soon as it is made and then a ladle full
of solder in a pasty condition slopped over it and quickly
wiped round the joint and then removed, so that it leaves
behind a coating of tin-rich solder which is drawn into the

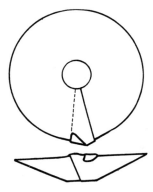

Fig. 20

depending on whether the operator prefers a lined or a surface pores of the joint completely filling them.

When using the pot method for a joint running vertically the solder cannot be poured over it, so the ladle is held about half an inch away from the joint and the solder splashed over it by means of a splash stick, which is usually a piece of curved iron with a wire handle similar to a $1\frac{1}{4}$in. carpenter's gouge ; an improvised tray, or 'catch plate,' is cut to the shape shown in Fig. 20 and bent to form a conical tray, the pointed ends being bent over to form clips that hold the set up in shape. This tray is fixed to the pipe just below the joint and prevented from slipping down by winding some thick string round the pipe just below it. Three or four pieces of lath are placed radially in this tray to break the droppings up and make them easier to remove, and these can be fixed by pouring a little solder round them ; the whole arrangement is shown in (5).

The blowlamp method of wiping a joint is almost the same as that just described, except that the joint is heated to almost melting point of the pipe by means of a blowlamp flame and a stick of solder held over the joint and melted by means of the blowlamp, at the same time rubbing it over the cleaned portion of the pipes and into the joint to

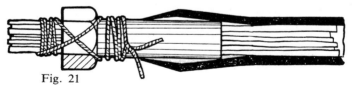

Fig. 21

tin them. The surplus solder is caught in the 'drip' cloth and worked round the joint to ensure that an even consistency is obtained. If necessary, more solder is now melted on to the joint and caught in the cloth, and when sufficient has been applied the stick of solder is laid aside and the mass of solder pushed back on to the top of the joint, the drip cloth being replaced by the wiping pad.

The mass of solder is now heated again and melted off the pipes, caught in the pad, and wiped round the joint, moulding it in the same way as that prescribed for pot wiping.

The soldering of liners to lead pipes is carried out in the same way. A bundle of thin sticks, or split laths, are inserted through the liner and into the pipe to hold it steady whilst the joint is being made, as shown in Fig. 21 ; the nut is prevented from falling back by tying it to the protruding sticks.

Car Body Soldering. This does not mean that solder is used to repair car bodies, but to hide the imperfections of the welded joints and to fill small dents, and is really a solder filler. This method of removing blemishes has increased greatly with the large firms mass-producing cars, as well as the small repair shops.

The weld or dent is first scratch-brushed down to bright metal and then acid fluxed. The spot is now heated with a blowlamp and a blob of solder melted on to it and, if the position is a vertical one, the molten solder is caught on a pad of tallowed hessian and rubbed, or wiped, over the cleaned portion, properly tinning it. Alternatively the area may be painted with "Frylux" or similar solder paint. Plumber's solder is now applied as for a wiped joint and the pasty solder is wiped and moulded into the shape and contour of the body to a smooth finish. If concave forms or angular shapes have to be sculptured, then a piece of bent metal may have to be used, and this should be coated with plumbago, or waxed to prevent the solder sticking to it. Whilst the form is being shaped, the solder must be kept in a plastic state by the occasional application of the torch or blowlamp. The final touches are imparted by means of a file or grind wheel.

When it is required to solder a large quantity of special metals, it is often more economical to use special materials in order to speed up the job, and in some cases it is often quite impossible to get a good joint unless special materials are used, and below are listed a number of metals that require special treatment.

Stainless Steel. Although stainless steels may appear bright and untarnished, most of them undergo rapid oxidization as soon as a new face is exposed by abrasion, and a flux must contain sufficient hydrochloric acid to maintain fully reducing conditions. The steel should be cleaned well and the special flux used that is mentioned in the chapter dealing with them.

Cast Iron. Remove the oxide skin by grinding or machining but not by sand blasting. De-grease thoroughly and use the flux recommended or a corrosive solder paint.

Aluminium Bronze and Silicon Bronze. Clean with abrasive and immediately flux with that recommended.

Aluminium. This is difficult under all conditions. Use a 95/5 tin-zinc solder, or Fry's "Fryal" or "L.M." solder, heat the metal until a blob of solder melts on to it, and then agitate the solder by scratching it with a hack-saw blade down to the base metal; it should eventually tin the aluminium, after which it may be soldered in the normal way. Alternatively, use a supersonic soldering iron, or bath.

Zinc Base Alloys. These cannot easily be soldered, but some claim to obtain satisfactory results using the solder suggested in Chapter 1, or aluminium solder or special fluxes with ordinary solder.

The chief difficulty that will be encountered in soft soldering will be the tinning of ferrous metals, but this difficulty can usually be overcome by repeated application of flux whilst the material is hot.

With cast iron, rubbing the moulder's solder into the surface of the metal with a glass brush dipped in flux is almost a certain cure; or for 100% success use a tinning powder.

CHAPTER 6

HARD SOLDERING AND BRAZING

THE chief difficulty experienced when hard soldering and brazing in a small workshop, that has not previously undertaken such work, is obtaining sufficient heat. Brazing a ½in. nipple on a copper pipe may not be found difficult, but hard soldering a copper flange on a 4in. diameter x 10 S.W.G. copper tube will be found to be another matter. Even the low melting point silver solders like "Easy-flo" or "Melt-esi" need a dull red heat. It is surprising, however, how much less heat an expert needs to do a job of a certain size, compared to a beginner. The three main considerations that reduce the heat required to braze a given size job are: —

(1) Careful lagging to prevent the escape of heat; this may consist merely of standing the job on firebricks; wrapping the job in asbestos cloth, or burying almost completely in coke. (2) Using the coke, not only to prevent the escape of heat but to add to it. (3) Using any additional heat in the right place.

Some workers do not like using coke for lagging or to help to supply heat because, they say, it spits and splutters and sticks to the job, but providing the coke is really dry (that is to say, it has been used on the hearth on previous jobs), then it is not likely to splutter to any extent, and although it may appear to adhere to the work, it will easily come off when the job is cool, or can be brushed off with a wire brush whilst hot. In order to obtain extra heat from the surrounding coke, the torch should be played over it, as it is moved about the job, and it may take some considerable time—10 to 15 minutes—before it really starts glowing.

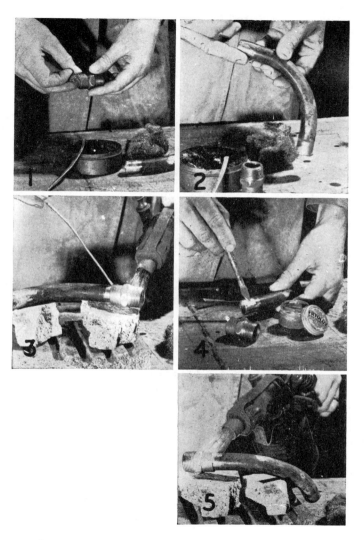

Plate No. 12. Soldering a Capillary copper pipe fitting

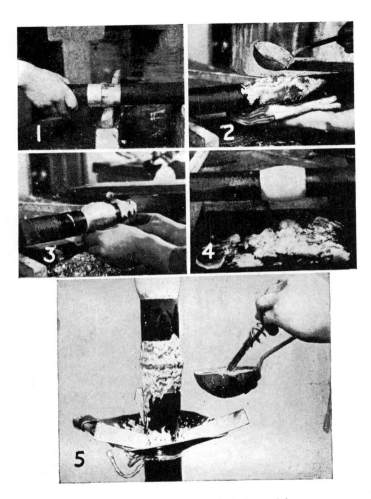

Plate No. 13. Process of wiping a joint

To give a very rough indication of the amount of heat required for various size jobs the following table gives an approximation:—

Article	Melting Point of Solder	Heat Source
16 S.W.G. wires	608	Small spirit blowlamp, or miniature self-blowing gas torch.
16 S.W.G. wire	850	
Mild steel strip 1″ x ⅛″	608	1 pint blowlamp. Bunsen type gas torch, of ½″ low-pressure injector.
Mild steel strip 1″ x ⅛″	850	No. 1 gas blow pipe with pressurized air supply.
2″ x 16 S.W.G. copper pipe	608	No. 1 gas blow pipe with pressurized air supply.
2″ x 16 S.W.G. copper pipe	850	No. 2 size gas blow pipe with pressurized air, " Flamemaster " with " Maxiflame " jet.
4″ x 16 S.W.G. copper tube and fitting	608	No. 2 size gas blow pipe with pressurized air, " Flamemaster " with " Maxiflame " jet.
4″ x 10 S.W.G. copper tube and fitting	850	Oxy-coal gas, acetylene torch, oxy-butane, oxy-acetylene.

The statutory coal gas pressure is one above 2in. water glass, and is normally kept between 5 and 10 inches for most towns' supplies. It can easily be measured by filling a deep bucket with water, connecting a rubber tube to the supply and noting at what depth the gas stops bubbling out; the orifice can be quite minute so that no great amount of gas is lost, but it is very necessary that the tube should connect with the supply at the point the torch is connected. Even then it is necessary to know the size of the supply pipes and distances from mains. The pressure may read 10 inches with the blow pipe off, but drop to as low as 2 inches with it on, if the supply from the mains is both long, and the bore of the pipe small.

Whereas with soft soldering a butt joint is rarely used because the solder is so weak, with hard soldering the butt joint is used quite extensively; silversmiths and copper-smiths not only use it but work on the metal afterwards as if there was no join in it, and for such work a very malleable solder is required. An instance of this kind of work would be in the making of a coffee-pot: a flat sheet of copper might be cut and bent to form a conical tube, and the joint then silver soldered or brazed; the tube might then be hammered into a curved shape if so desired, without detriment to the join.

Basically there are only two types of joints, the butt and the lap, all others are combinations of these two to a greater or lesser degree. A butt joint must be very carefully made and longitudinally should be slightly concave (see B Fig. 22). When joining thin metals up to 16 S.W.G. perfect alignment is not essential if the joint can be planished afterwards.

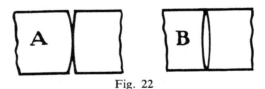

Fig. 22

Scarf joints are usually used for jointing band saws, and resistance brazing is often used for this purpose, the brazing strip or silver solder being preplaced in the form of fluxed foil.

The width of the joint in a lapped joint depends on a number of factors but a rough guide is to make the joint at least three times the thickness of the metal being joined.

Joints over 20 S.W.G. should have the edges nicked or notched with a triangular file to allow penetration of solder. (See Fig. 23.)

When making a joint, if the metal has been properly cleaned, fluxed and the correct amount of heat applied

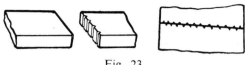

Fig. 23

in the correct place. the solder should always run into the joint, being drawn there by capillary attraction, and not over other portions of the article being soldered; but to prevent the danger of this happening, the metal outside the joint may be painted with Fullers earth, mixed with very weak size; heat-resisting aluminium paint; or a lead pencil rubbed over these portions. However. if too much flux is used it is likely to spread over to these parts and float the 'spoil' off. So use only the minimum.

Like soft solders, hard solders can often be preplaced, but with hard solders the parts to be joined are often working parts which must be kept in perfect alignment, as in a built-up crankshaft for a small petrol engine; but clearances of 0.001in. to 0.003in. are required to make a satisfactory capillary joint using most hard solders, and it will be obvious that with such clearances the joint will not be self-aligning, and a jig must be used whilst the article was being brazed. In order to overcome this difficulty, the arrangement shown in Fig. 24 is suggested. This represents two parts of a built-up crankshaft, and the solder is preplaced by forcing wire into a shallow groove cut in the spigot end of the big-end bearing. This spigot is turned down to a good push fit into its housing and the groove cut for the solder and the wire forced into it, after which a further 0.001in. is turned off the spigot, except for a small portion at either end, and it is these lands which register the spigot accurately in its hole. In order to allow the steam to escape from the flux, it might be found necessary to cut a very shallow groove along one of the lands, but in small

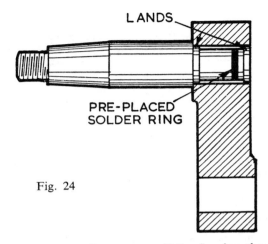

LANDS

**PRE-PLACED
SOLDER RING**

Fig. 24

work this is not usually necessary if the flux has the surplus water dried out of it before the job is assembled. Alternatively, the whole length may be given the necessary clearance and then parallel knurled to form a good push fit.

When joining two unlike metals together special care must be taken that the different coefficients of expansion do not destroy the working clearances of the joint, and endeavour should be made to construct the joints in such a manner that you can see what is happening as shown in Fig. 25, "A" being the incorrect way and "B" the correct. With lap joints a fillet adds practically no extra strength,

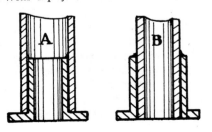

Fig. 25

but with a right angle butt joint it is worth while. It is almost impossible to make a joint without leaving a small fillet of solder, and in silversmith work this sometimes detracts from the finish. To overcome this trouble a small chamfer should be filed on the corner of the joining metal (see Fig. 26), but the size of these chamfers can only be ascertained by trial with the actual solder being used.

Fig. 26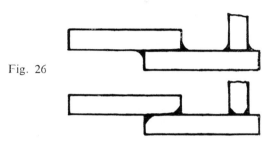

When brazing two pieces of metal together that are of different thicknesses, the flame of the torch should be played mostly on the thicker of the two so that they are both kept at the same heat. If one piece reaches the melting point of the solder before the other trouble will result; this is usually manifested by the solder running over the hotter piece of metal instead of into the joint. This means extra work when the job is being cleaned up. The solder will always flow to the hottest part of the job, and this should be the joint itself. When a long joint is being soldered, as soon as one end has been brought to the melting temperature, the flame of the torch should be slowly moved along the joint so that the molten solder will follow it, more solder being added as required.

When repetition work has to be carried out it is well worth while to make jigs to hold the parts together whilst they are being brazed, but for 'one off' jobs this procedure is hardly worth while, and the parts must be either wired,

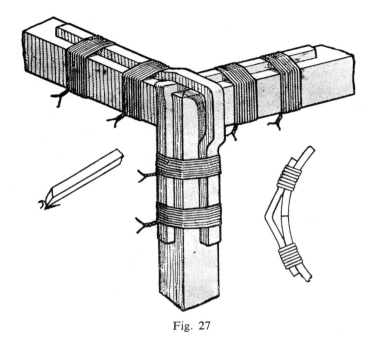

Fig. 27

pinned, or clamped together. Some methods of doing this
are shown in Fig. 27, including a silversmith's 'stitch.'
This is used to position light articles on curved surfaces,
such as the dome ring on a model locomotive boiler.
The 'stitch' is made by marking the outline of the object
on the article, to which it is to be joined, and with a graver
form a curl of metal by pushing the graver forward to the
marked line, commencing about 1/16in. from it; four such
stitches will hold a circular object in place, and if they
show after soldering they may be filed off with a smooth file.
When soldering ferrous metals in special ovens, with reducing
atmospheres and pure copper brazing strip, preplaced with

no flux, this strip is capable of penetrating even interference fits.

When clamping or wiring objects, care must be taken to allow for expansion ; otherwise considerable distortions will result. This trouble can be minimized in two ways: (1) By heating the whole article being brazed as evenly as possible ; (2) Using a small but very hot flame, and localizing the heat as much as possible.

Turning now to the practical side of hard soldering and brazing, it would be as well first to carry out a simple exercise to discover exactly what your available apparatus is capable of doing. Take a length of $\frac{3}{4}$in. x 16 S.W.G. mild steel about 6in. long, bend over the last half inch so that it is at right angles and clamp this in the vice, so that the strip lies horizontal, then clean up the top surface of the steel with emery cloth. Cut a $\frac{1}{4}$in. length of "Easy-flo" wire and the same length of 18 S.W.G. brass and copper wire.

Place these pieces of solder on the top of the steel strip spaced 1in. apart, and cover with the appropriate flux: "Easy-flo" flux for the "Easy-flo" solder and powdered borax for the other two. This can be sprinkled on in powder form. Now play the flame of your blow pipe on the underside of the steel concentrating under the "Easy-flo" to start with ; note that as soon as the steel becomes a dull red, the solder melts into a globule and then immediately spreads out over the steel forming a pool about half an inch in diameter.

Next concentrate the flame under the brass wire, and see if you can melt it. You may or may not ; it will depend on how hot your flame is and not on the size of the flame, because with a comparatively small surface like the steel strip, with a large flame, most of the heat will pass either side of it. If you find you cannot melt the brass wire by applying the heat underneath, try playing the flame directly on to the solder, and you will most likely find that it melts at once, but it only forms into a globule and does not spread out over the steel; this usually means that the solder has reached its melting point, but the strip has not, the heat being conducted away too rapidly from it. So now try another experiment: remove the strip from the vice and lay it on the coke of hearth and play the flame on both the coke and the steel. As soon as the coke has reached a bright glow, concentrate the flame on the steel and you should have no difficulty in making the brass solder melt and flow over the strip, but the copper wire may still refuse to run and the only alternative left now is to pile the coke all round the strip, only leaving the small portion of steel exposed on which lies the copper wire. Now get the flame moving around this saucer of coke until it is really glowing well, and then concentrate on the steel, and you should have no difficulty in making the copper run. Do not cover up too much of the steel strip; otherwise you will not be able to conduct sufficient heat to it. As an indication for the beginner, "Easy-flo" should run when the steel shows a dull red in dim day light, the brass at a cherry red, and the copper at a bright orange.

Next let an actual job be considered. Suppose it is required that a brass nipple has to be soldered onto a copper pipe, and as it is required to carry high pressure steam, soft solder is ruled out. Shall we silver solder it or braze it ? On a small job like this the heat required should not be a worry, and the only concern is whether the brass nipple will stand a 50/50 brass solder. It most likely would not but to save expense, a silver solder with a low silver content can be used, the melting point will be higher but not dangerously high. Such a solder would be "Sibralloy," a Johnson, Matthey product, with a liquidus temperature of 694° C. Unfortunately, this solder cannot be manufactured as a wire, so a circlip of preplaced solder cannot be used, and it must be treated as a straightforward brazing job. The end of the copper pipe is first cleaned with steel wool, and also the inside of the nipple, which can best be done by winding some strands of steel wool round a piece of stick. A small amount of the correct flux—in this case "Tenacity 4a"—is placed on a piece of clean glass and a drop of water added, just sufficient to damp it. It is then left for ten minutes, when it will be found that the paste has become thinner and may or may not require the addition of more water. The end of the pipe and the inside of the nipple are now painted over with the flux, using a camel hair brush to do so. If the flux does not take, heat the pipe and nipple, and try again. As soon as one coat is dry paint on another, and then the nipple is threaded over the end of the pipe. The pipe should now be stood against some support with the nipple downwards and resting on a firebrick. The flame of the torch is played on the assembly, keeping it moving around, mostly on the nipple, but endeavour to keep the whole assembly at an even heat; hold the torch in the left hand, so that you will be able to apply the solder with the more agile right hand. Whilst the nipple is heating up, heat the tip of the stick of "Sibralloy" and dip it into the dry flux, so that some of the powder adheres to it and then when the nipple is dull red, hold the tip of the solder in the flame and against the joint; it should heat up very quickly and melt onto the joint. "Sibralloy" is not a universal solder and should be used with discretion—the elongation is only 10%.

The points to watch are these: don't overheat the job and melt the nipple, and if you are in doubt at what heat the nipple will melt, try melting a small piece of brass rod. This will give you an indication of its melting point.

The flame of the torch should only brush the end of the solder, which should be melted by the heat conducted from the work ; otherwise you will most likely melt off much more than you want and cover the nipple with solder which will take a lot of removing. When it does melt, if the heat is enough, the solder disappears so quickly into the joint that the beginner imagines it has dropped off the end and missed the joint, and he then adds more. It is also possible to mistake molten flux for molten solder, so watch carefully. If a blob of solder breaks off the stick and sticks to the pipe or nipple as a semi-plastic mass, this indicates that the heat is not sufficient, but if it stays like a globule of mercury it may still mean the work is not hot enough, or that it is covered with a coating of oxide, and if the addition of flux or more heat does not help, the molten solder should be agitated with a pointed piece of steel wire. If the solder runs over the nipple and not into the joint it usually indicates that the pipe is not hot enough ; if, and this is more likely, the solder adheres to the pipe and does not run into the joint, then the nipple is not hot enough.

However, on a small job like this it is far more likely that the job would be over-heated rather than under.

Although "Silbralloy" was recommended for this job, it was only chosen to save cost, and a number of other more expensive solders could have been used.

Another example of silver soldering that will bring up a number of problems would be the making of a copper cream jug, later to be silver-plated. If it is thought that the construction of a silver-plated cream jug is unlikely, then you can call it a copper oil measure. Anyway, the problems met in making such an article are likely to be met manufacturing other articles of a similar type.

Let it be supposed that the only torch available is a self-blown low-pressure coal gas torch, and therefore for this job it will be necessary to use a low melting point solder of the "Easi-flo" type and another, say G6, of slightly higher melting point. The copper for the body is cut to shape from say 20 S.W.G. material and the joint edge

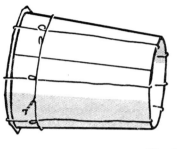 

Fig. 28

carefully filed straight, making certain the ends of the joint touch when the body is bent round to shape. The body should then be wired, as shown in Fig. 28, so that the joint cannot spring open; and the best wire to use for this is chrome nickel wire, either new or from an old electric fire, of 24 or 26 S.W.G., because this will stand the heat far better than plain or iron wire which is very easy to burn through unless great care is taken and the flame kept on the move all the time. The joint should have been carefully fluxed with the correct flux before carrying out the wiring-up process. The wired-up body is now laid on the hearth in a horizontal position with the joint upwards. A length of G6 wire is scraped to remove any oxide and painted with flux, and then cut into lengths about ¼in. long, and these pieces of silver solder are laid along the joint at about 1in. intervals. The flame of the torch is applied all around and about the body until it is seen that the flux is commencing to melt; then the flame is applied to the joint, but on the inside, keeping the flame moving but giving a little more heat to one end so that the solder starts to run at that point first; then move the flame along the inside of the joint at such a speed that the pieces of solder melt and run into the joint as it moves below them.

The solder will run towards the hottest part, and this being on the inside of the body, it will be certain of running right through the joint. The whole should be cooled by plunging into water and the wire then removed. If it is found that the binding wire has been soldered to the body it can usually be pulled off, but if this is found to be impossible it should be cut on either side of the joint and the remaining portion and also any surplus solder carefully filed away. The body is now placed over a round bar, held in the vice, and the joint planished—hammered— flat. It should be mentioned here with butt joints like the above that when made with thicker metal the edges should be notched very slightly with a three-cornered file about every $\frac{1}{8}$ in. or less, to let the solder through to the other side, and get right into the joint (Fig. 23).

The bottom edge is now filed true, and the bottom itself cut out so that it is slightly larger than the diameter of the body, the joint area cleaned, fluxed, and wired to the body as shown in Fig. 28. The wiring is not essential, but it does prevent the body slipping at the crucial moment. Quarter inch lengths of fluxed solder are again placed round the joint but this time they are supported by that portion of the bottom that protrudes beyond the body, and solder of a lower melting point than the G6 is used, such as "Easi-flo," so that when heat is applied the joint already soldered will not be sprung; but care must be taken not to overheat the job, or that very thing will happen.

It is as well to support the bottom on three small pieces of firebrick, or asbestos, so that the flame can get underneath, otherwise it will be found difficult to bring the bottom up to the correct temperature without overheating the body, unless laid on its side; but in that case the wires may loosen and the bottom come away. The jug is then quenched in water and pickled in a 10% solution of sulphuric acid to remove oxide and flux residue, after which the protruding portion of the base can be trimmed off with shears and filed flush.

The position of the handle is marked out with a pencil and the two 'stitches' made at the top and the bottom to make certain it does not move when the heat is applied.

The job is now pickled once more and it is complete, except for a final clean up and polish.

A brazing job that is extremely useful, and at the same time simple to carry out, is the tipping of lathe tools. The tips are usually purchased rough shaped to size, and it is then necessary to mill a mating recess in the end of the tool shank. Small pieces of copper foil, or preferably silver solder, are cut to shape to act as shims (that slightly protrude when placed behind and under the tip) on all abutting

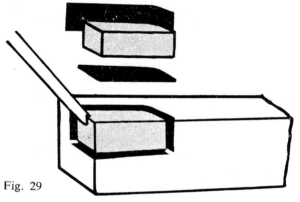

Fig. 29

surfaces. These are scraped and fluxed, as is also the recess on the shank and the tip itself, these portions having been degreased and cleaned before doing so.

The near end of the tool shank is held firmly in the vice so that three-quarters of it is clear of the jaws. Heat is now applied to the tip, which should be held lightly in place with a length of $\frac{1}{8}$in. steel rod, forked at the ends, whilst

the flux boils (see Fig. 29). At least half of the shank
should be well heated to prevent sudden cooling of the
tip, which should be brought to the melting point of the
solder as quickly as possible; as soon as the foil is seen to
run the heat is removed and the tip pressed in to the recess
by the tip of the forked rod, and held there until the
solder freezes.

Only solders and brazing strip having a high ductility
should be used for this work to accommodate the thermal
stresses set up, due to the different expansion coefficients of
the two metals when in use.

When brazing carbide tungsten tips only low temperature melting point solder is advised, such as "Easy-flo"
No. 3.

Tackling really large and heavy jobs like brazing a model
boiler for a 5in. gauge locomotive with a 13 S.W.G. barrel
and a 10 S.W.G. door plate, the man who has nothing but
a paraffin blowlamp is in for a difficult and hot job.
A five pint blowlamp by itself will not be enough and
preferably a second one of a similar size should be brought
on to the job as well, although if the second lamp is skilfully
used by a helper who knows what he is doing, it can be
done with a one pint size as the second string.

Because a boiler is continually under stress from varying
pressures and heats, only those, repeat only solders with
good ductility should be used. Whilst the job is light the
higher melting point solders should be used; not only will
this save cost in solder but will prevent a part already
soldered from coming unstuck when a second portion is
being brazed, and if you find you cannot heat a solder of say
750° C. melting point when less than half of the parts of the
boiler are assembled, then it is not likely that you will have
sufficient heat available to melt the lower melting point
solders when the whole boiler is assembled for the final
joints to be brazed.

If rivets are going to be used to position the various parts on a job like this, it is very necessary that they should be of copper, otherwise they will not stand up to the continual expansion and contraction that takes place, and will eventually loosen and cause a leak. A low melting point silver solder should be used for the screwed nipples to take the various boiler fittings, because these are often of low melting point brass, and it is quite easy to burn them. When brazing the backhead, unless an old oildrum is used as a hearth, it will be found impossible to bury the boiler deep enough to bring the coke up level with the backhead; the alternative is to get an old tray or similar piece of metal, cut a hole in it, and push the barrel through this so that the wrapper is left projecting on top of the tray which should now be supported on bricks, and then coke piled all round the wrapper. (See Fig. 30.) If now one blowlamp is played on the backhead and the other on the surrounding coke, there should be no difficulty in getting

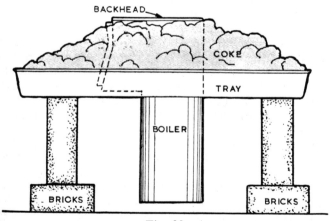

Fig. 30

the heat to melt the solder. But don't try to do this job in a confined space, because you will need all the ventilation you can get, and even on a cold day you will most likely finish up in your shirt sleeves.

Another point to remember is that you will require some sort of holder for the solder, because when the job is really hot you will not be able to get your hand within 18 inches of it.

As each stage of the boiler is completed it should be pickled in 10% solution of sulphuric acid, the acid being added to the water; on no account should the parts be put into the pickle hot, unless you want to take severe risks of acid burns. This especially applies to the tube assembly, because the acid heated in the small confines of the tube, form steams which can shoot the acid a great distance with dire results. Although hot pickling is quicker, it is far safer to pickle the job cold for, say, half an hour or more.

After pickling, the job should be well washed out with cold water, and cleaned up with pumice powder, "Vim," or some other such material.

If, when the job is tested under pressure, some pinholes are found, these can best be dealt with by marking the spot and then drilling and tapping a 10 B.A. hole and screwing in a length of 10 B.A. screwed copper rod smeared with flux and soft solders. Finally, after all staying has been carried out, the heads of the stays inside and out should have soft solder run around them. Use high temperature solder.

To tackle such a large piece of brazing using nothing else than a paraffin blowlamp is to tackle it the hardest way, and it will be found to be a comparatively easy job to do if acetylene-air, oxy-coal gas, or oxy-acetylene is used. In the latter case use a larger nozzle, at least twice the size used with steel, and the gas pressure should be reduced until the flame is silent or nearly so. The outside of the flame envelope is used and not the inner cone as is normally used for welding; and it should be slightly oxidising.

Because it has often been suggested that a copper-zinc-silicon alloy such as "Sifbronze" be used for the above type of work if oxy-acetylene is available, it would be as well to point out here that such a process is not brazing or soldering, but welding, and is therefore outside the scope of this book. The manufacturers of "Sifbronze" can supply a brazing strip that is free flowing under the trade name of "Sifcupron"; the former has a melting point of 800/850° C. and the latter 750° C.

If the joints are rather open a solder with a long plastic range should be used and not heated above this range so that the solder fills up the spaces and does not run through them.

If the worker has not available the heat necessary to silver solder a boiler, the joints can be riveted with copper rivets spaced say $\frac{1}{4}$in. centres and then soft soldered.

The chief difficulty that will be encountered in hard soldering will be the oxidising of the solder and burning of the flux by bringing them into direct contact with the flame. *Make the metal melt the solder,* not the flame, and if possible heat the joint by conduction, that is by playing the flame on the underside of the joint.

Most cast irons cannot be silver soldered, but Malleable and Mehanite irons usually can be; it is advisable to make a test on the particular type of cast iron before doing a particular job.

The frontispiece shows the set-up for brazing a large model locomotive boiler. The barrel has been wrapped with asbestos tape, and the fire box buried in coke, having only that portion to be brazed exposed. One worker operates a coal gas blow pipe and the other adds further heat with a paraffin blowlamp

TABLE No. 1

Alloy Tin-Lead % Tin	Liquidus Degrees C.	Solidus Degrees C.	Plastic Range	Tensile Strength Tons □"	Shear Strength Tons □"	Elongation % on 4"	Izod Impact	Elect., Conduct.	Viscosity at 28° Poises	Surface C. Tension Dynes
100	232	232	0° C.	0.94	1.28	1.28	14.2	13.9	0.0112	546
63	183	183	0°	3.35	2.78	2.78	14.8	11.9	0.0133	490
50	214	183	29°	2.75	2.56	2.56	15.5	11	0.0142	476
40	236	183	55°	2.75	2.22	2.22	14.1	10.2	0.0150	471
30	255	183	74°	2.66	2.06	2.06	11.5	9.5	0.0160	469
0	327	327	0°	0.89	0.90	0.90	5.6	7.91	Solid	Solid

By Courtesy of the Tin Research Institute

PROPERTIES OF JMC SILVER BRAZING ALLOYS   APPLICATIONS OF JMC SILVER BRAZING ALLOYS

Brazing alloy	Melting range °C.	Tensile strength tons per sq. in.	Vickers hardness	Elec. Conductivity per cent. IACS	Numerical order of cost 1=highest	Notes on characteristic applications	JMC brazing flux used in conjunction where required
Grade A, BS 206	690-737	25	105	27	3	For high conductivity electrical joints. High silver and low zinc contents permit use in reducing atmosphere furnaces without flux.	Tenacity flux 4A
Grade B, BS 206	698-788	26	120	22	6	Good general purpose alloy where long plastic range and comparatively high melting point are not disadvantageous.	Tenacity flux 4A
Easy-flo (Grade C, BS 206)	620-630	30	131	21	4	A eutectic-type alloy offering maximum ductility with low melting point and ability to join dissimilar metals. See Data Sheet 2121.	Easy-flo flux
*Easy-flo No. 2	608-617	30	135	20	5	An all-purpose alloy having the lowest silver content consistent with a low, short melting range and the ability to join dissimilar metals. See Data Sheet 2122.	Easy-flo flux
Easy-flo No. 3	634-656	30	140	20	4	Special alloy for tungsten carbide tool tipping. See Data Sheet 2128. Also used on steels which are difficult to 'wet.'	Easy-flo flux
*Argo-flo	605-651	32	136	20	7	A quaternary alloy of general application, intended for use where a long plastic range is desirable or where the use of high silver alloys is economically impracticable. See Data Sheet 2124.	Easy-flo flux
B 6	790-830	28	121	20	10	The highest melting silver brazing alloy in the popular JMC range for use where elevated temperatures are met in service.	Tenacity flux 4A

TABLE No.

PROPERTIES OF JMC SILVER BRAZING ALLOYS   APPLICATIONS OF JMC SILVER BRAZING ALLOYS

Brazing alloy	Melting range °C.	Tensile strength tons per sq. in.	Vickers hardness	Elec. Conductivity per cent. IACS	Numerical order of cost 1 = highest	Notes on characteristic applications	JMC brazing flux used in conjunction where required
C 4	740-780	34	156	21	9	Suitable for both ferrous and non-ferrous jointing and used where two-stage brazing calls for a subsequent joint with Easy-flo in close proximity.	Tenacity flux 4A
D 3	700-740	24	143	21	8	Suitable for both ferrous and non-ferrous work and retained in the popular range for its intermediate melting point.	Tenacity flux 4A
G 6	705-723	28	121	28	2	The silver solder used by silversmiths on hall-marked silver ware, for which a low melting point and white colour are required.	Easy-flo flux
Eutectic	778	22	90	70	1	The binary silver-copper alloy used in vacuum tube joints and also for flux-free brazing in reducing atmosphere furnaces.	Tenacity flux 4A
Sil-fos	625-780	45	187	8	10	For flux-free brazing copper, with flux on copper alloys or in reducing atmosphere without flux. Unsuitable for steel or nickel alloys. See Data Sheet 2131.	None on copper, elsewhere Tenacity flux 4A
†Silbralloy	638-694	35	195	6	11	For oxy-acetylene flux-free brazing of copper at low cost. Unsuitable for steel and nickel alloys, but suitable for copper alloys with flux. See Data Sheet 2132.	None on copper, elsewhere Tenacity flux 4A

The properties given above relate to the alloys in the cast condition. The values are thus representative of the materials as deposited in a brazed joint.

* Covered by British Patent 558,873.   †Covered by British Patent 538,297.

SOLDER MANUFACTURERS

Sir Wm. Burnett & Co. (Chemicals) Ltd.,
   Great West Road, London
       •

Bakers flux

The British Oxygen Co. Ltd.,
   Hammersmith House, London W.6

Industrial gases, oxy-acetylene torches, brazing strip

The Du-Bois Co. Ltd.,
   15, Britannia Street, Kings Cross,
   London, W.C.1

Cored solders

Enthoven Solders Ltd.,
   Dominion Buildings, South Place,
   London, E.C.2

All types of soft solders and
fluxes

Fry's Metal Foundries Ltd.,
   Tandem Works, Merton Abbey,
   London, S.W.19

All types of soft solders and
fluxes

Johnson, Matthey & Co. Ltd.,
   73-83, Hatton Garden, London, E.C.1

Silver solders and fluxes.
"Easy-Flo"

Multicore Solders Ltd.,
   Mellier House, Albemarle Street,
   London, W.1

Cored solders

The Sheffield Smelting Co. Ltd.,
   95, Arundel Street, Sheffield 1

Brazing strip, silver solders,
fluxes, "Meltezi"

Suffolk Iron Foundry (1920) Ltd.,
   Sifbronze Works, Stowmarket

Brazing strip, oxy-acety-
lene torches

Eutectic Alloys Ltd.,
   North Feltham Trading Estate, Fagg
   Road, Feltham, Middx.

All types of silver solder
and brazing Alloys

Author's Note

Since writing Chapter 4, two new types of soldering irons have appeared on the market. The "Instantaneous" type which has a bit, which is part of a one turn secondary of a step down transformer. The efficiency of these depend on the design of the joint between the "bit" and the single turn. Many of these work well when new, but if a slight oxide skin forms between the joints of the removable bit and the turn; the voltage is so low—a mere fraction of one volt—that it cannot overcome the resistance of this oxide skin, and the efficiency quickly falls off.

The other new type is one operated from a low voltage transformer, and laying the iron across the transformer switches off the current. A comparatively high heating current is used which heats the bit up in a few seconds to soldering temperature, the joint is then made and the bit replaced onto the transformer rest which switches off the current.

If used for anything other than quick joints, the iron would overheat, but this can be an advantage because high melting point solders can be used if required, even some silver solders.

INDEX